SHAYNE WARD

GW00393799

WISE PUBLICATIONS
PART OF THE MUSIC SALES GROUP
LONDON/NEW YORK/PARIS/SYDNEY/COPENHAGEN/BERLIN/MADRID/TOKYO

PUBLISHED BY
WISE PUBLICATIONS
14-15 BERNERS STREET, LONDON, W1T 3LJ, UK.

EXCLUSIVE DISTRIBUTORS:
MUSIC SALES LIMITED
DISTRIBUTION CENTRE, NEWMARKET ROAD,
BURY ST EDMUNDS, SUFFOLK, IP33 3YB, UK.

MUSIC SALES PTY LIMITED
120 ROTHSCHILD AVENUE, ROSEBERY,
NSW 2018, AUSTRALIA.

ORDER NO. AM986194
ISBN 1-84609-634-0
THIS BOOK © COPYRIGHT 2006 WISE PUBLICATIONS,
A DIVISION OF MUSIC SALES LIMITED.

EDITED BY CHRIS HARVEY.
MUSIC ARRANGED BY JACK LONG.
MUSIC PROCESSED BY PAUL EWERS MUSIC DESIGN.

PRINTED IN THE EU.

WWW.MUSICSALES.COM

THAT'S MY GOAL

WORDS & MUSIC BY
JÖRGEN ELOFSSON, BILL PADLEY & JEREMY GODFREY

finally found that some-thing ____ worth ___ reach-ing for. I'm not

here ___ to say I'm sor - ry, ___ I'm not here ___ to lie to you. ___ I'm

here ___ to say I'm rea - dy, ___ that I've fin - ally thought it through. ___ I'm not

here ___ to let your love ___ go, ___ I'm not giv-ing up, oh, no. I'm

10

ev - er._____ I'm not here___ to say I'm sor - ry. I'm not

here___ to say I'm sor - ry,___ I'm not here___ to lie to you.___ I'm

here___ to say I'm rea - dy,___ that I've fin - ally thought it through.___ I'm not

here___ to let your love___ go, I'm not giv-ing up, oh,___ no._____ I'm

NO PROMISES

WORDS & MUSIC BY
JONAS SCHRODER & LUCAS SIEBER

Hey, ba - by, when_ we are_ to - geth - er doing things_____ that we love,_ ev - 'ry time you're near_ I feel_ like I'm_ in Hea - ven, feel-ing high_

here to-night. ____

I don't wan-na run ____ a-way; I wan-na stay ____ for-ev - er, through

time and time. ____ No pro - mis - es. ____

I don't wan-na run a-way, ____ I don't wan-na be a - lone. ____

No pro - mis - es,_____ ba - by.

Now I need to hold you tight;_____ now and for - ev - er, my love.____

No pro - mis - ses.__

I don't wan - na run a - way,__ ba - by; you're the one I need to - night.__

16

No pro - mis - es,_____ ba - by. Now I need to hold you tight;

I just wan - na die__ in your arms_____ here to - night__

here to - night.____

STAND BY ME

WORDS & MUSIC BY
SAVAN KOTECHA & ANDREAS ROMDHANE

18

me,   hold__ on_____ and nev - er__ let me

go?_____   Will you stand_____ by

me?_____   With you   I know I be - long,__   when the sto - ry gets

told.   2. When day turns told.   I am

stand_____ stand by me? Will I be a

part of your life____ when the sto-ry gets told._____ Stand by

me,_____ stand by me;_____ won't you

stand,_____ stand by me?_____ Stand by

ALL MY LIFE

WORDS & MUSIC BY
KARLA BONOFF

I will nev-er find an-oth-er lov-er sweet-er than you,____ sweet-er than you;____

and I will ev-er find an-oth-er lov-er more pre-cious than you,____

YOU'RE NOT ALONE

WORDS & MUSIC BY
JOSEPH BELMAATI, MICH HANSEN, JONAS SCHRODER & LUCAS SIEBER

1. She's get-ting out of bed at half past ten, she starts to comb her hair:
2. She's wait-ing for the bus, it's twelve fif-ty nine, she's sit-ting on her own:

— just an or-di-na-ry day.
— just an or-di-na-ry day.

feel - ing lost___ in - side,___ you're not a - lone.___ (You're not)___

___ You're not a - lone.___ When your world is fall - ing down,___ I will

be the one___ a - round; you're not a - lone.___

34

I CRY

WORDS & MUSIC BY
JÖRGEN ELOFSSON, PER MAGNUSSON & DAVID KREUGER

36

WHAT ABOUT ME

WORDS & MUSIC BY
GARRY FROST & FRANCES SWAN

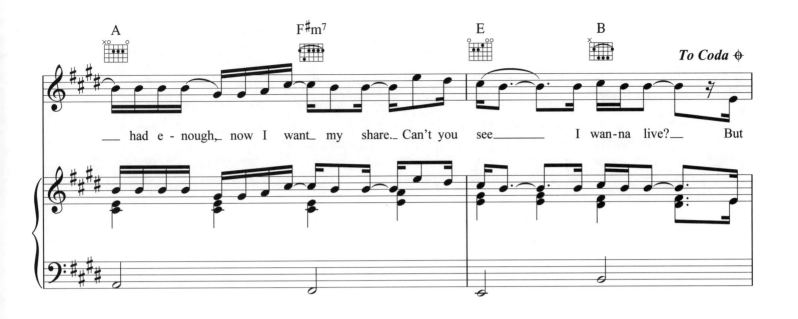

had e-nough, now I want my share. Can't you see_____ I wan-na live?___ But

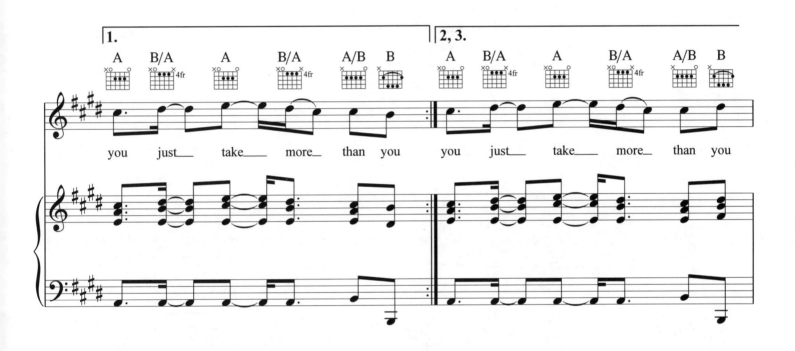

you just___ take___ more__ than you   you just___ take___ more__ than you

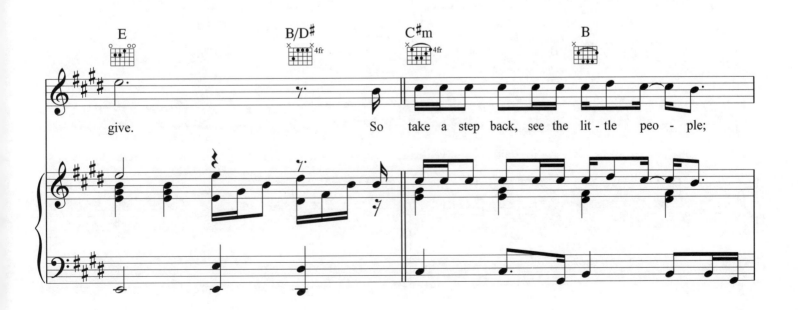

give.   So take a step back, see the lit-tle peo-ple;

44

BACK AT ONE

WORDS & MUSIC BY
BRIAN MCKNIGHT

SOMEONE TO LOVE

WORDS & MUSIC BY
JÖRGEN ELOFSSON & ANDERS BERGSTROM.

54

SOMETHING WORTH LIVING FOR

WORDS & MUSIC BY
SAVAN KOTECHA & ANDREAS ROMDHANE

57

59

A BETTER MAN

WORDS & MUSIC BY
SAVAN KOTECHA & JOSEF LAROSSI

1. Un-til the o-ceans all run dry, un-til the stars fall from the
2. sun, I'll still be-lieve you are the
3. all. I'll al-ways catch you when you

sky, ev-en if words don't seem to rhyme,
one. No mat-ter what we're go-ing through,
fall and, if the hard times get too much,

NEXT TO ME

WORDS & MUSIC BY
ALISTAIR TENNANT, JOSEPH BELMAATI, MICH HANSEN, MIKKEL SIGVARDT & REMEE

66

OVER THE RAINBOW

WORDS BY E.Y. HARBURG
MUSIC BY HAROLD ARLEN

123456789